JOHN DINNEEN

# Party Games and Rotten Tricks

ILLUSTRATIONS:
LOUIS SILVESTRO

ANGUS & ROBERTSON PUBLISHERS

# Prizes & Forfeits

When games are played at a party it is a good idea to have lots of little prizes for the winners.

These can be wrapped and put in a large tin or box.

A person can then have a lucky dip when they win.

**Ideas for party prizes:**

*Fake spiders, bats and mice, fancy erasers, notebooks, coloured pencils, badges, party whistles, bubble pipes, crazy straws, Slime, small magic tricks, small puzzle games, sweets, hairclips and ribbons, transfers, balloons, bubble gum.*

**FORFEITS**

When somebody loses a game they can be made to take a forfeit.

Forfeits can be written on pieces of paper which are folded and put into a large tin or box. This is an unlucky dip for the losers.

**Here are some ideas for forfeits:**

# Pairs

*Can you find your partner amongst all the rest?*

**YOU WILL NEED:**

*A card for each player.*

**How to play PAIRS**

**1.**
*Cut the cards from paper or card, make them into pairs by drawing or writing something on each one. Here are some ideas for cards:*

**2.**
*Shuffle the cards and give one to each player.*

**3.**
*On the word go, everyone must find the person with the matching card.*

**4.**
*When everybody has a partner, games such as feeding baby (page 5) and the paper clothes game can be played.*

**Other ideas for your cards:**

*Animals and young, e.g. (cow—calf)*

*Words that go together, e.g. (foot—ball)*

# The Floating Feather

*Keep the feather in the air.*
*If it lands on you, beware!*

## FOR THIS GAME YOU WILL NEED:

*A small fluffy feather (or a small piece of tissue paper will do).*

## How to play
## THE FLOATING FEATHER

**1.**
*Players sit as close together as they can.*
**2.**
*Somebody drops the feather from above.*
**3.**
*Everybody blows or flaps their hands to keep the feather floating.*
**4.**
*If the feather touches somebody then they must pay a forfeit decided by the person on their right.*

# Feeding Baby

*It is great fun to play this game and just as funny to watch.*

**YOU WILL NEED:**

**1.**
*A bowl of cornflakes (broken biscuits or crumbled cake will do).*
**2.**
*A wooden spoon for each player.*

**How to play
FEEDING BABY**

**1.**
*Two people feed each other with the cornflakes, while others watch the fun.*
**2.**
*Other pairs can also play at the same time.*
**3.**
*See which pair can eat all their cornflakes first.*

1

2

3

# Pass the Parcel
## (with forfeits)

*When the music stops, start unwrapping. You will find a present or a forfeit every time.*

**YOU WILL NEED:**

**1.**
*A prize.*

**2.**
*Five (or more) pieces of paper with forfeits written on.*

**3.**
*Small presents such as sweets, balloons, or stickers.*

**4.**
*Wrapping paper (newspaper will do).*

**5.**
*Sticky tape.*

**6.**
*A record player or radio.*

**1**

**2**

**3**

**4**

**5**

**6**

## How to make the PARCEL

**1.**
Wrap the prize in layers of wrapping paper.
**2.**
Under each layer put either a small present or a forfeit.
**3.**
When you have a large enough parcel you are ready to play the game.

**1**

**2**

**3**

## How to play PASS THE PARCEL

**1.**
Choose somebody to work the record player, stopping and starting the music when everyone least expects it.
**2.**
Everybody else sits in a circle. While the music plays the parcel is passed around the circle.
**3.**
When the music stops, the person holding the parcel takes off one layer of wrapping paper. If they get a present they keep it. If they get a forfeit they must carry it out.

**4.**
The music is then restarted and the game continues.
**5.**
The person who unwraps the last layer wins the prize.

# The Matchbox Game

*This game is not as easy as it looks!*

**YOU WILL NEED:**
***The outer part of a matchbox for each player.***

**How to play**
**THE MATCHBOX GAME**

**1.**
*Players kneel down and place their matchboxes in front of them.*
**2.**
*Measure the distance by putting forearms flat on the floor, elbows touching knees. The box is placed just beyond a player's outstretched fingers.*
**3.**
*On the word "Go", players put their hands behind their backs and must then get the matchbox on their noses, without moving forward on their knees.*
**4.**
*The first person to pick up the matchbox with their nose wins.*

**1**
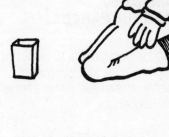

**2**

Elbow touching knee

Fingers outstretched

**3**

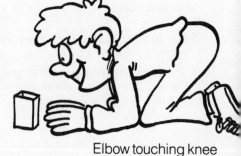

Players' knees must stay in the same place

# The Egyptian Mummy

This is a good party trick to play on your friends.

## YOU WILL NEED:

**1.**
A sheet, a rolled-up newspaper.
**2.**
Some towels.
**3.**
An assistant (who will be the mummy).

## How to play
## THE EGYPTIAN MUMMY

**1.**
Everybody leaves the room except you and the assistant. The assistant lies on the floor.
**2.**
Make a false head and shoulders with the towels.
**3.**
Cover with the sheet.

**4.**
Remove the assistant's shoes and leave them sticking out near her or his head.
**5.**
Each person enters the room in turn, bows to the mummy's head three times and says each time: "O ancient mummy from Egypt, I worship you."

**6.**
Before they finish the mummy rises up and bonks them with the newspaper!
**7.**
Once players have been bonked they can stay to watch others, but they must be sworn to secrecy.

# Whirligig

*Give your friends a fright.*

**YOU WILL NEED:**

**1.**
*Two short, blunt pencils.*
**2.**
*An elastic band.*

**How to make
a WHIRLIGIG**

**1.**
*First put the pencils through the
elastic band.*
**2.**
*Next, hold one pencil firmly and
wind the other one round until it's
tight.*
**3.**
*Now carefully place your wound-
up whirligig under a heavy object
such as a book.*
**4.**
*Watch the fun when somebody
lifts the book!*

**1**

**2**

# Tangles

*This game will have your friends tied up in knots.*

**FOR EACH GUEST YOU WILL NEED:**

**1.**
*A long piece of string or wool.*
**2.**
*A small present wrapped up.*
**3.**
*A card with the guest's name on.*
**4.**
*Sticky tape.*

**How to play TANGLES**

**1.**
*With sticky tape, attach each name card to an end of the pieces of string.*
**2.**
*Attach the presents to the other ends.*
**3.**
*Wind the strings around the room.*
**4.**
*Leave the presents where they can be seen.*
**5.**
*On the word "Go", guests find their name cards and follow their string to their present, winding up the string as they go.*

**1**
**2**
**3**
**4**

# Noah's Ark in the Dark

*This game is a hoot and is best with at least eight players.*

## YOU WILL NEED:

**1.**
*A piece of paper for each player.*
**2.**
*A pencil and a box.*

## How to play
## NOAH'S ARK IN THE DARK

**1.**
*Write the names of animals on the papers so that there are two of every animal. (If there is an odd number of players make three papers of one animal).*
**2.**
*Fold each piece of paper and put them into a tin or box.*
**3.**
*Each player takes one and looks at it without showing anyone else.*
**4.**
*Now switch the lights off.*
**5.**
*Everybody makes the noise of their animal and must find their mate. Other sounds are not allowed.*
**6.**
*The losers are the last pair to find each other.*

**1**

**2**

# Chimps' Tea Party

*Here is a trick to play on your party guests.*

**YOU WILL NEED:**

*A tape recorder.*

**How to play
CHIMPS' TEA PARTY**

**1.**

*At tea time, secretly record your guests eating their food.*

**2.**

*Later on, say that you are going to play a recording of the chimps' tea party at the zoo.*

**3.**

*Watch their faces when they hear themselves!*

# Greetings, Your Majesty

*An identification game that requires at least six people.*

**How to play
GREETINGS, YOUR
MAJESTY**

**1.**
*One person is blindfolded.*

**2.**
*Another is secretly chosen and, in
a disguised voice, says:
"Greetings, Your Majesty!"*

**3.**
*The blindfolded player must try to
guess who spoke.*

**4.**
*If they fail, another person says:
"Greetings, Your Majesty!" And so
on.*

**5.**
*When the blindfolded player
guesses somebody correctly this
person takes a turn to be
blindfolded.*

GREETINGS
YOUR
MAJESTY

# The Great Chocolate Race

*This game will really get you and your friends in a tizz!*

**YOU WILL NEED:**

**1.**
*A dice and shaker.*

**2.**
*A hat, scarf and gloves.*

**3.**
*A knife, fork and plate.*

**4.**
*A bar of chocolate in its wrapping.*

**How to play
THE GREAT
CHOCOLATE RACE**

**1.**
*Put all the items (except the dice and shaker) on a chair.*

**2.**
*Each player throws the dice in turn.*

**3.**
*As soon as someone throws a six they rush over to the chair and put on the hat, scarf and gloves. Then they try to both unwrap and eat the chocolate with the knife and fork.*

**4.**
*The other players continue to throw the dice.*

**5.**
*When another player throws a six, they rush to remove the hat, scarf and gloves from the first player, put them on and try to eat the chocolate as before.*

**6.**
*The first player rejoins the others.*

**7.**
*This continues until all the chocolate is eaten, or the players are worn out.*

**1 2 3 4**

# Balloon Burst

*These two games will make your party go with a bang.*

**Game 1**
**YOU WILL NEED:**

**1.**
*One balloon for each player.*
**2.**
*Two chairs.*

## How to play
## BALLOON BURST 1

**1.**
*The players divide into two teams and line up at one end of the room.*
**2.**
*Put all the balloons behind the two chairs.*
**3.**
*On the word "Go", the first player in each team runs up, puts a balloon on a chair, sits on it and bursts it.*

**4.**
*The player runs back and it is the next player's turn.*
**5.**
*The first team to finish wins.*

**Game 2**
**FOR EACH PLAYER**
**YOU WILL NEED:**

**1.**
*A balloon.*
**2.**
*Some string about 40 cm long.*

## How to play
## BALLOON BURST 2

**1.**
*Everybody ties a balloon to their ankle.*
**2.**
*On the word "Go", players try to burst each other's balloons.*
**3.**
*The last person with a blown-up balloon wins.*

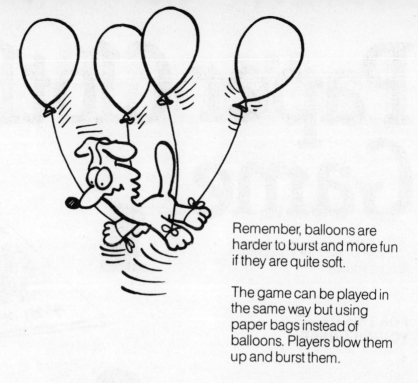

Remember, balloons are harder to burst and more fun if they are quite soft.

The game can be played in the same way but using paper bags instead of balloons. Players blow them up and burst them.

# Paper Clothes Game

*Dress your partner in paper as fast as you can.*

**1**

**2**

## FOR THIS GAME YOU WILL NEED:

**1.**
*Some old newspapers.*
**2.**
*Paper clips (sticky tape will also do).*

## How to play the PAPER CLOTHES GAME

**1.**
*Players divide into pairs, each with some newspapers and paper clips.*
**2.**
*On the word "Go", one of each pair dresses the other in the newspaper.*
**3.**
*Paper clips hold the newspaper together.*
**4.**
*The first pair with a player fully dressed wins the game.*
**5.**
*Only faces, hands and feet are allowed to show.*

A more challenging version of the game is for both players in each pair to dress each other at the same time.

### Fashion Parade

**1.**

*First choose someone to be the judge.*

**2.**

*Players divide into pairs and dress each other in newspaper.*

In this version it is the best outfit that wins the contest.

# A Watery Trick

*Give a friend this tricky problem to solve.*

### A WATERY TRICK

**1.**
*Fill two paper cups with water.*
**2.**
*Put them on the backs of your friend's hands.*
**3.**
*Now tell him or her to remove both cups without spilling any water.*

(The answer is carefully to drink the water in one cup and then remove the other with the free hand. It is best to try this out in the kitchen!)

# The Ring Game

## YOU WILL NEED:

*Some string and a ring.*

## How to play
## THE RING GAME

**1.**
*Everybody sits in a circle with one person in the middle.*
**2.**
*Put the string through the ring. Tie the ends of the string to form a big enough circle for everyone to hold. Sing a song to help it along.*
**3.**
*All players except the person in the middle, hold the string with both hands, one of them hiding the ring.*

**4.**
*Can the person in the middle guess who has it?*
**5.**
*Don't keep the ring too long but try to pass it on without it being seen, for, if the middle player guesses right and you've got the ring, it is your turn in the middle. If players holding the string all shuffle their hands, it adds to the confusion.*

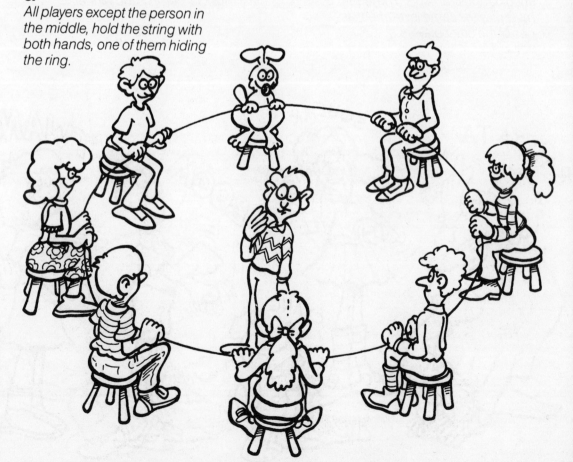

# Crazy Concert

*Everybody takes an imaginary musical instrument, pretends to play it and makes the right sound.*

## HERE ARE SOME INSTRUMENTS TO CHOOSE FROM:

*Drums, violin, trombone, triangle, cymbals, trumpet, harp, flute.*

*People can take turns to suggest a well-known tune to play.*

## How to play CRAZY CONCERT

**1.**
*First choose a leader. He or she faces the other musicians.*
**2.**
*Everybody starts playing their imaginary instruments. The leader must play the same instrument as one of the other players.*

**3.**
*The leader can, at any time, change his instrument. If, for example, he changes from playing a piano to playing a trumpet, all trumpet players must immediately start playing a piano.*
**4.**
*If the leader then changes to the cymbals all cymbal players must change to trumpets.*
**5.**
*The leader continues to change instruments. Anyone that forgets to change or plays the wrong instrument is out of the game. The last musician left in is the winner.*

# Musical Mimes

**YOU WILL NEED:**

*A recording of your favourite singer for this miming contest.*

**How to play
MUSICAL MIMES**

**1.**
*First choose someone to be the judge.*
**2.**
*Everybody takes turns to mime to the recording.*
**3.**
*The best performance wins the contest.*

# Minefield

*Play this trick and you will see someone treading carefully.*

**YOU WILL NEED:**

*Six plates and a blindfold.*

**How to play
MINEFIELD**

**1.**
*Lay the plates on the floor.*
**2.**
*Now choose a victim, show them the plates and tell them: "You must walk through the minefield when I say 'Go' without treading on a plate."*
**3.**
*Now blindfold them.*
**4.**
*QUIETLY pick up the plates.*
**5.**
*Watch the fun as they tip-toe through the minefield which is not there!*

Victim

Minefield

# Word Tennis

*This is a game for two people at a time to play.*

## How to play
## WORD TENNIS

**1.**
*A third person gives two players a subject, for example: vegetables.*
**2.**
*One of the players starts off: "Cabbage".*
**3.**
*The other player must say another vegetable within three seconds.*

**4.**
*They carry on until one of them cannot think of another vegetable or repeats one, thus losing the game.*
**5.**
*The winning player can then challenge a new player to a game.*

You can make cards out of paper or card, each giving a different topic, and choose the subjects using these.

# The Tasty Game

Find out how good your taste buds are.

## YOU WILL NEED:

Food cut into small pieces and a blindfold.

Some food suggestions are lemon, cheese, chocolate, onion, liquorice, green beans, carrot strips, dried apricot, half a cube of sugar.

## How to play
## THE TASTY GAME

**1.**
Blindfold the first player.
**2.**
Pop a piece of food into their mouth and ask them to chew it carefully.
**3.**
Can they guess what food it is?
**4.**
Now let the next player have a go.

# The Short Arm

*Bet somebody that you can make their arm shorter.*

## THE SHORT ARM

**1.**
*Tell them to stand so that they can just touch a wall with fingers outstretched.*

**2.**
*They now rub their elbow of this arm with the other hand.*

**3.**
*Their arm will now appear to be a little shorter!*

The person must not move during the trick.

# The Rising Arm

*Here is how to make somebody's arm rise up on its own.*

## THE RISING ARM

**1.**
*The person presses their arm hard against a wall and counts to 10.*

**2.**
*When they move away from the wall their arm will rise up on its own!*

# Knock Kneed Racing

*You don't need knock knees for this race, but it helps.*

**YOU WILL NEED:**

**1.**
*Two piles of large size coins.*
**2.**
*Two wastepaper bins.*
**3.**
*A clock.*
**4.**
*Tape or string for a starting line.*

# How to
# RACE KNOCK KNEED

**1.**
One person is chosen to start and time the race. Everybody else divides into two teams. (It is best with three or more people in a team.)

**2.**
Place the bins at one end of the room. The teams line up at the other end, each with a pile of coins.

**3.**
Tape can be put on the floor for a starting line.

**4.**
On the word "Go", the first player in each team puts a coin between their knees, walks with it to the bin and drops it in.

**5.**
They then run to the back of their team and the second player starts, and so on. After five minutes, the team with the most coins in its bin wins.

**6.**
No touching coins with your hands once over the start line.

**7.**
But, if a coin is dropped, the player must pick it up and return with it to the start line to begin their turn again.

# Racing Fish

*See who can race their fish the fastest.*

**YOU WILL NEED:**

**1.**
*Thin paper (newspaper will do).*
**2.**
*Scissors.*
**3.**
*Some magazines.*

**How to play
RACING FISH**

**1.**
*Cut fish shapes out of the paper, one for each player. You are now ready to start a fishy race.*
**2.**
*Everybody lines up at one end of the room.*
**3.**
*On the word "Go", each player wafts their fish along with a magazine.*
**4.**
*First fish over the finishing line wins.*

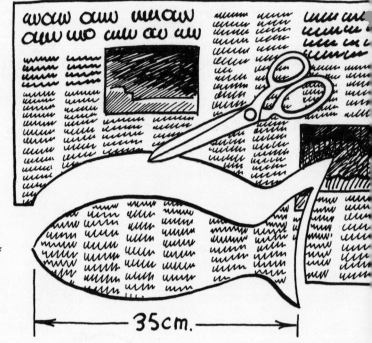

35cm.

# The Smell Game

*How well can you smell?*
*Test your own and your friends'*
*sense of smell.*

**YOU WILL NEED:**

**1.**
*Pieces of material cut into 15 cm squares.*
**2.**
*Elastic bands or string.*
**3.**
*Things that smell. Some suggestions are fresh pine shavings, cocoa, cloves, fresh cabbage, coffee, onion, curry powder, orange peel.*

**How to play**
**THE SMELL GAME**

**1.**
*Put each item on a separate material square and tie it up. (Extra material or paper may be put inside.)*
**2.**
*Tag each bag with a number for identification and hang them from a line just over head height.*
**3.**
*Without touching the bags, can your friends guess what is in the bags?*
**4.**
*They can write down on a piece of paper what they think they have smelt.*

# Shopkeeper

## How to play SHOPKEEPER

**1.**
One person leaves the room.
**2.**
Everybody else chooses a shop.
**3.**
The person is called back into the room.
**4.**
On the count of three, the shopkeepers together call out something sold in their shops.

**5.**
If the player does not guess one of the shops, shopkeepers call out something else sold in their shops.
**6.**
This is repeated until she or he guesses a shop.

# Blow Ball

## YOU WILL NEED:

*This game, for two or more, just needs a ping pong ball and a table.*

## How to play
## BLOW BALL

**1.**

*You and your opponent sit either side of the table and, to start off the match and each round, the ball is placed in the middle of the table.*

**2.**

*Blow as hard as you can and score a goal every time the ball goes over your opponent's edge.*

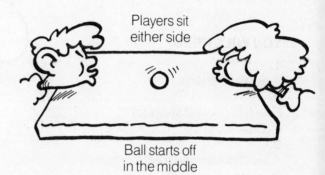

Players sit either side

Ball starts off in the middle

**3.**

*Remember, touching the ball is not allowed.*

# Suck-a-Sweet

## YOU WILL NEED:

**1.**

*A bowl of Smarties.*

**2.**

*A straw and a saucer for each player.*

## How to play
## SUCK-A-SWEET

**1.**

*See how many sweets you can suck up with a straw. . . and drop into a saucer.*

**2.**

*See who can collect the most sweets in two minutes flat.*

**3.**

*Players keep all the sweets they suck up.*

# Beetle

This game is just crawling with fun for two or more players.

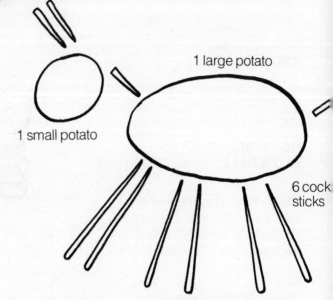

1 small potato

1 large potato

6 cocktail sticks

## YOU WILL NEED:

**1.**
A dice and shaker.

**2.**
Four half cocktail sticks (or toothpicks) for each player.

**3.**
A small potato and a large potato for each player.

**4.**
Six cocktail sticks (or toothpicks) for each player.

## How to play BEETLE

**1.**
Put the potatoes and cocktail sticks in the middle.

**2.**
Each player throws the dice then passes it to the next person.

**3.**
On throwing a six a player takes a large potato and can start making a beetle.

**4.**
To make the complete beetle you must throw all the numbers on the dice. These each stand for a different part of the beetle:

one  = the head and neck
two  = for each feeler
three = for each front leg
four = for each back leg (there are four)
five  = the tail
six  = the body

For example, if a player throws a one after a six, a neck and head may be added to the body. If the player follows his or her six with a four, one of the four back legs may be added.

**5.**
You will see that a two (for the feelers) is no use until you have a head.

**6.**
The first person to make a complete beetle wins.

# Sausages

*You will split your sides when you play this game.*

**How to play SAUSAGES**

**1.**
*First choose someone to be "it".
Everyone else takes turns to ask
"it" a question.*

**2.**
*"It" must always answer:
"Sausages",* **without laughing**.

**3.**
*"It" counts up the number of questions
that he or she answers before laughing
and letting someone else be "it".*

> SAUSAGES.

> 'HAT'S YOUR NAME?

> WHAT'S ON YOUR HEAD?

> WHAT DO YOU WANT FOR YOUR BIRTHDAY?

# Sooty Face Trick

*This rotten trick will make almost everyone laugh.*

### YOU WILL NEED:

**1.**
*An adult's help to prepare for this trick.*
**2.**
*A candle.*
**3.**
*A table and two chairs.*
**4.**
*Two small plates.*

### How to play
### SOOTY FACE TRICK

**1.**
*Get your adult to hold the underside of **one** of the plates over a lighted candle until it is covered with soot.*
**2.**
*Leave both plates on the table. When your friends arrive, choose a victim who is asked to sit opposite you at the table.*

Sooty plate

**1**

**2**

**3.**

*This game is better if you first distract your victims by telling them that you are going to test their powers of observation. They must do exactly what they see you do.*

**4.**

*Then, blink your eyes a few times, tap your left-hand middle finger, lean sideways, and so on, always pretending to pay careful attention to the victim's moves.*

**5.**

*When you think the victim is feeling confident that he or she is doing everything right, pick up the plate and carefully hold it up, keeping the underside towards the other person.*

**6.**

*Your victim will pick up the other plate.*

**7.**

*Now rub the underside of your plate with your fingers and rub your fingers on part of your face.*

**8.**

*Repeat this a few times.*

**9.**

*The result will be a sooty face and lots of fun!*

Victim

# More Potato Fun

Lots of weird animals can be made with potatoes and cocktail sticks.

## FOR THIS GAME YOU WILL NEED:

**1.**
Clean potatoes.
**2.**
Cocktail sticks (or toothpicks).
**3.**
Somebody to be the judge.

## How to play MORE POTATO FUN

**1.**
Divide up the potatoes and cocktail sticks amongst the players. Make sure that everyone has big and small potatoes.
**2.**
Everyone tries to make the strangest animal. When the last player has finished, the judge chooses the winner.
**3.**
Here are some ideas:

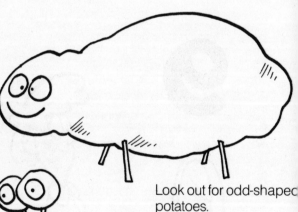

Look out for odd-shaped potatoes.

Caterpillar

# The Horrid Finger

## YOU WILL NEED:

**1.**
*A matchbox.*
**2.**
*Red ink.*
**3.**
*Cotton wool.*
**4.**
*Talcum powder.*

## How to play
## THE HORRID FINGER TRICK

**1.**
*Remove one end of the matchbox tray with scissors.*
**2.**
*Line matchbox bottom with cotton wool splattered with a little red ink.*
**3.**
*For a grim effect, dust your index finger with white talcum powder and spatter a little more red ink around its base.*
**4.**
*Shut the matchbox and put your finger in the open end.*
**5.**
*Tell your victim that you have found someone's finger on the floor. . .*
**6.**
*Slide open the matchbox and reveal the finger inside.*

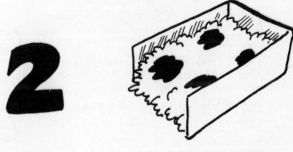

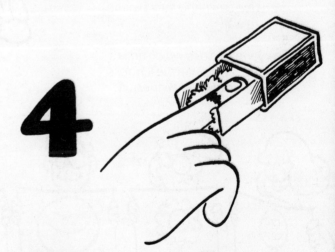

# Artists

*This game is rather arty.*
*It will be a winner at your party.*

**YOU WILL NEED:**

*Paper and crayons for each player.*

**How to play**
**ARTISTS**

**1.**
*Everyone sits around the room*
*with their paper and crayons.*
*Players should not be able to see*
*each other's drawings.*
**2.**
*One person is chosen to be*
*leader. They slowly draw a picture*
*while they describe what it looks like.*
**3.**
*Everybody else draws what they*
*think it looks like.*
**4.**
*When the drawing is finished*
*everyone can hang their picture*
*up on a wall.*
**5.**
*Everyone decides which artist's*
*drawing is most like the leader's,*
*and this artist is the winner.*

# Sounds

Listen to the sounds. How many can you guess?

**YOU WILL NEED:**

*Various objects for making noises with. Here are some suggestions:*

**1.**
*Rubbing a comb.*
**2.**
*Stirring a drink.*
**3.**
*Snapping a carrot.*
**4.**
*Pouring rice (or water) into a bowl.*
**5.**
*Tearing or cutting paper.*
**6.**
*Rustling paper.*
**7.**
*Bouncing a ball.*
**8.**
*Twanging a ruler.*

**How to play SOUNDS**

**1.**
*Make these noises hidden behind a screen (e.g. a sofa) or around a corner. See how many of them your friends can guess.*
**2.**
*If you have a tape recorder you can record other sounds such as a door creaking, a sewing machine, sawing wood, a dripping tap, etc.*

**1** RRRRR

**2** CHINK CHINK

**3** SNAP

**4** SSS SSSSS RICE

**7** BOING

**8**

# Murder in the Dark

*A horrid scream, the victim lies dead. Can the detective find the murderer?*

**2**

## YOU WILL NEED:

**1.**
*A tin or box.*

**2.**
*A piece of paper for each player — write a* **D** *on one and an* **M** *on another. All the remaining pieces of paper are blank.*

## How to play
## MURDER IN THE DARK

**1.**
*Fold the pieces of paper and put them into the tin.*

**2.**
*Each player then takes one and looks at it without showing anyone else.*

**3.**
*The player with the paper marked* **M** *is the murderer.*

**4.**
*The player with the paper marked* **D** *is the detective.*

**5.**
*Only the detective reveals him or herself and leaves the room.*

**6.**
*Now switch the lights off. The other players walk about the room.*

**7.**
*After a few minutes the murderer taps someone on the shoulder and that person becomes the victim.*

**7**

**8.**
The victim screams and falls down dead. All the other players must stand still. Only the murderer can quickly move to another position.
**9.**
On hearing the scream the detective enters the room, switches the lights back on, and tries to discover the murderer.

**10.**
The detective can question anyone with as many questions as he or she likes. For example, he or she might ask: "Why are you looking so guilty?" or: "Why did you murder him?" Only the murderer can tell lies but must confess if asked: "Are you the murderer?"
**11.**
The detective can only ask two people this question. If he fails to discover who did the horrible deed then the murderer can safely reveal himself.
**12.**
The game can then be repeated.

# Nelson's Eye

*In the dark pass Nelson's parts.*
*Feel his liver, lungs and heart!*

## FOR THIS HORRID GAME YOU WILL NEED:

*Various objects to be parts of Nelson's body. For example:*

**1.**
*Eye (peeled grape).*
**2.**
*Brain (cabbage or cauliflower).*
**3.**
*Lungs (two soft balloons).*
**4.**
*Tongue (piece of meat or liver).*
**5.**
*Hand (rubber glove filled with wet sand).*
**6.**
*Ear (dried apricot).*
**7.**
*Intestines (raw sausages).*
**8.**
*Veins (cooked spaghetti).*

## How to play NELSON'S EYE

**1.**
*With the lights off, players sit in a circle. Pass the first object, for example the peeled grape, to one of the players and say: "Here is Nelson's eye."*
**2.**
*The eye is then passed round the circle. Then you can give players the next bit of Nelson, and so on.*

**1**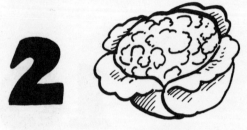

**2**

**3**

**4**

**5**

**6**

**8**

**7**

# Zany Zoo

*What strange animals
   are in the zoo.
There are some rather odd
   people too.*

**FOR THIS GAME YOU WILL
NEED:**

*Strips of paper and crayons.*

**How to play
ZANY ZOO**

**1.**
*The first player draws an animal's
head at the left side of the paper.*
**2.**
*This player folds the paper to hide
the head and passes the paper to
the next player.*
**3.**
*He or she draws the next part of
the animal, folds the paper and
passes it on.*
**4.**
*This is repeated four or more
times. The last player draws the
animal's tail end. The paper is
then unfolded and the animal
revealed.*

*You can also draw funny people too.*

# Four Rotten Old Tricks

*These tricks always give someone quite a surprise.*

### 1. APPLE PIE BED

**1.**
*Fold the top sheet in half and make it impossible for someone to get inside.*
**2.**
*Tuck the sheet in on both sides. When the covers are replaced the top sheet now looks like two.*

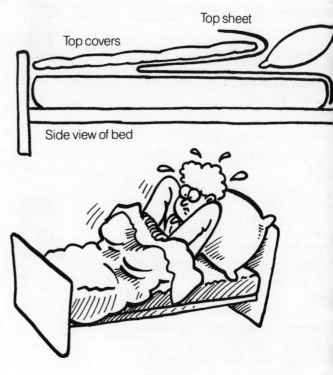

Top covers · Top sheet

Side view of bed

### 2. SEWN-UP SLEEVES

*Sew up the end of a sleeve or trouser leg with a few large stitches.*
*P.S. The stitches can be easily removed afterwards.*

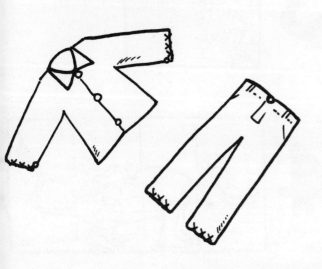

### 3. BLACK EYE TELESCOPE

**1.**
You will need a cardboard tube (for example from a kitchen roll) and some black paint.
**2.**
Paint the tube black and allow it to dry.
**3.**
When you are ready to play the trick on someone paint one end of the tube black.
**4.**
With the paint still wet, tell your victim that you have a magic telescope. When they look down the painted end the result will be a black eye.

### 4. TRICK PARCEL

Wrap a small present in as many layers of wrapping paper as you can and make a big parcel.

# Broomstick Challenge

*Tie your friends in a knot with this tricky stunt.*

**YOU WILL NEED:**

*A broom handle. (If you find this too difficult you can use a long flexible cane.)*

**How to play**
**BROOMSTICK CHALLENGE**

**1.**
*Palms facing downwards, thumbs to the front.*
**2.**
*Pass the broomstick over your head.*
**3.**
*Lift your right leg up, put it around your right arm, behind the stick.*
**4.**
*Pass your left hand over your head and step out of the stick.*

It is a good idea to practise beforehand so that you can show your friends how easy it really is.

The aim is to start off like this . . .

. . . and to finish like this without altering your grip (although your hands can slide along the broom handle).

*ANGUS & ROBERTSON PUBLISHERS*

*Unit 4, Eden Park, 31 Waterloo Road,*
*North Ryde, NSW, Australia 2113, and*
*16 Golden Square, London W1R 4BN,*
*United Kingdom*

*First published in Australia*
*by Angus & Robertson Publishers in 1986*
*First published in the United Kingdom*
*by Angus & Robertson in 1986*
*Reprinted 1986*

*Copyright © John Dinneen, 1986*

*National Library of Australia*
*Cataloguing-in-publication data.*

*Dinneen, John.*
  *Party games and rotten tricks.*

  *ISBN 0 207 15314 0.*

  *1. Games — Juvenile literature. 2. Tricks —*
*Juvenile literature. I. Silvestro, Louis.*
*1953-   . II. Title.*

*793'.01'922*

*Typeset in 11pt Helvetica by The Type Shop*
*Printed in Australia by the Globe Press Pty Ltd*

# Titles in this series include:

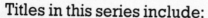

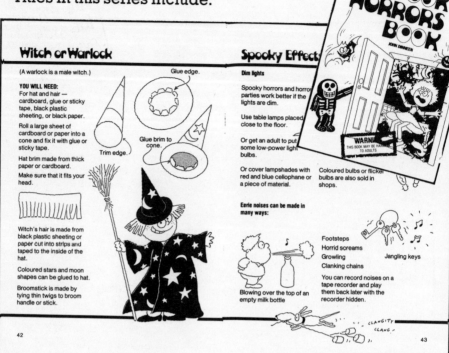

## Witch or Warlock

(A warlock is a male witch.)

**YOU WILL NEED:**
For hat and hair —
cardboard, glue or sticky
tape, black plastic
sheeting, or black paper.

Roll a large sheet of
cardboard or paper into a
cone and fix it with glue or
sticky tape.

Hat brim made from thick
paper or cardboard.

Make sure that it fits your
head.

Witch's hair is made from
black plastic sheeting or
paper cut into strips and
taped to the inside of the
hat.

Coloured stars and moon
shapes can be glued to hat.

Broomstick is made by
tying thin twigs to broom
handle or stick.

Glue edge.

Glue brim to
cone.

Trim edge.

## Spooky Effect

**Dim lights**

Spooky horrors and horror
parties work better if the
lights are dim.

Use table lamps placed
close to the floor.

Or get an adult to put
some low-power light
bulbs.

Or cover lampshades with
red and blue cellophane or
a piece of material.

Coloured bulbs or flicker
bulbs are also sold in
shops.

**Eerie noises can be made in
many ways:**

Footsteps
Horrid screams
Growling
Clanking chains

Jangling keys

You can record noises on a
tape recorder and play
them back later with the
recorder hidden.

Blowing over the top of an
empty milk bottle

CLANGITY
CLANG

42

43

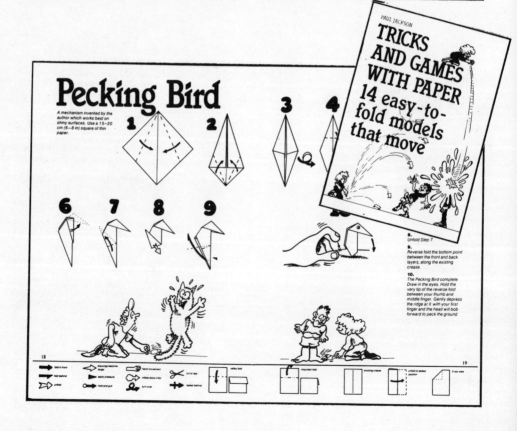

# Pecking Bird

A mechanism invented by the
author which works best on
shiny surfaces. Use a 15–20
cm (6–8 in) square of thin
paper.

**1** **2** **3** **4**

**6** **7** **8** **9**

**8.**
Unfold Step 7.

**9.**
Reverse fold the bottom point
between the front and back
layers, along the existing
crease.

**10.**
The Pecking Bird complete.
Draw in the eyes. Hold the
very tip of the reverse fold
between your thumb and
middle finger. Gently depress
the ridge at X with your first
finger and the head will bob
forward to peck the ground.

18

19

# Lowdown Logic I

**1.**
Thirty birds sit on the upper branches of a tree. A so-called 'sportsman' fires three volleys of buckshot at the birds, killing half of one-third of their number.
Can you quickly say how many birds remain?

**2.**
There are six sandwiches in a brown paper bag. How can you give six hungry young kids a sandwich each and have one left in the bag?

**3.**
Imagine you have nine cakes and four large paper bags. How can you put an odd number of cakes into each bag without cutting any of the cakes or tearing the bags?

**4.**
"What day is it?" asked the prisoner suddenly of her cellmate ruminating on the bottom bunk.
"Goodness," replied the other. "Well let's see — the day after the day after tomorrow will be the day before the day before Sunday."
Can you work it out before the short-tempered prisoner lashes out?

**5.**
How many months have 28 days?

**6.**
Two fathers and two sons went fishing. Each caught a fish but they landed only three fish in all. How is this possible?

**7.**
When Mike was first going out with Milly he carved their initials inside a heart on a tree trunk 1 m from the ground. When Mike and Milly were married exactly a year later the tree had grown 20 cm. During the following years it doubled its growth rate annually. How high was the heart on Mike and Milly's tenth wedding anniversary?

# Leading

# Cut the Cube

This 20 cm cube is patterned all over. Pecos William is about to cut it into smaller cubes with 5 cm sides.
Some of the cubes will have 3 patterned faces, some 2, some 1, and some none. How many will there be of each? Help William find out before he is bitten by a maddened bull terrier.

# Man on a Bed

This figure comes from the Torres Straits. After you have made the Man on a Bed, chant:
*Man on a bed, man on a bed
Lies asleep, lies asleep,
The bed breaks.
When the bed breaks, the man falls out!*

**1**
*Do Opening A. Keep the index loops near the tips of your index fingers.*

2.
Your thumbs go under the index loops to get the near little finger strings and return under the strings of the index loops.

3.
Your little fingers hook down the far index strings. Your little fingers get the far thumb strings. They return through the strings of the index loops.

**2**

**3**

**4**

**5**

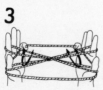

**How**
**Koochie Man**

Begin again, but this time put a twist (make an X) in the string loop as you put it on your hands in Position 1. Now complete Opening A and follow steps 1 to 6. You make him dance by turning your hands so that first your thumbs and then your little fingers come close together.